If you took all the people who fell on the floor when they read this book and laid them end-to-end, you'd have a very long line of people. It'd be a silly thing to do, but at least you'd know who to avoid at a cocktail party.

~ **Gail Englert**, Retired National Board Certified Teacher and
NCTM Board Member 2002–05

Vennebush never fails to entertain! His work is worthy of a limerick:

Patrick was faster than most folks
In learning a collection of math jokes.
They roll off his tongue
Faster than bells that have rung,
So he published some books for us slow pokes.

~ **Johnny Lott**, Professor Emeritus,
University of Montana, and NCTM President 2002–04

If you're above the 90th percentile, you'll chuckle or groan at all of the jokes in this book. If you're above the 50th percentile, you'll chuckle or groan at some of them. But if you find that you're not chuckling or groaning at any of them, well…

~ **David Barnes**, Associate Executive Director, NCTM

Laughter is good for your health. Really, it is! That's why I'm very glad that Patrick Vennebush has done it again! Take your own journey through *MORE JOKES 4 MATHY FOLKS*; but regardless of the path you take, you'll smile, laugh out loud, and think about ways to use or adapt some of these jokes in your own classroom or personal repertoire.

~ **Francis (Skip) Fennell**, Professor Emeritus,
McDaniel College, and Past President AMTE and NCTM

Patrick Vennebush proves why he will never be eaten by cannibals—he would surely taste funny. The second volume of mathy jokes will bring smiles to the faces of teachers and groans from students when you use these jokes in class!

~ **Fred Dillon**, Institute for Learning,
University of Pittsburgh

Henny Youngman and Leonhard Euler walk into a bar. Patrick Vennebush faithfully captures their conversation in this collection of old saws, with all the corollaries worked out, along with some new results. He proves that math, unfairly the dread of many, is more than ready to have a good laugh. Like a good joke, good math has a set-up that invites the reader to wonder what is coming, then — pow! — a zinger of a punchline that surprises and delights. Vennebush shares humor found in this intersection that will give a chuckle, maybe a groan, and some sneaky insights.

~ **John Golden**, Associate Professor,
Grand Valley State University, and
Blogger at http://mathhombre.blogspot.com

While everyone loves to laugh, most people wouldn't expect that to take place in a math classroom. This book fixes that problem with humor that kids and adults will chuckle about. Check out these jokes out, and share them with your students and colleagues!

~ **Robert Kaplinsky**, Math Teacher Specialist,
Downey Unified School District

What an amazing collection of jokes, problems and stories that are "plays" on numbers, their names, relationships among them, and how they are used in many fields and by folks in varying professions. I spent lots of time trying to figure out how the answers to questions were determined — strange relationships! — and had my colleagues and students try to solve them, too. That figuring-out process produced many laugh-out-loud results. You don't have to be a math aficionado to love this book.

~ **Carole Greenes**, Professor and Director of the PRIME
Center, Arizona State University

MORE JOKES
4 MATHY FOLKS

G. Patrick
Vennebush

Another collection of math jokes
from the author of the best-selling
MATH JOKES 4 MATHY FOLKS

Robert D. Reed Publishers
P.O. Box 1992
Bandon, OR 97411
Phone: 541-347-9882; Fax: -9883
E-mail: 4bobreed@msn.com
Website: www.rdrpublishers.com

Cover Designer: Cleone Reed
Book Designer: Susan Leonard

ISBN 13: 978-1-944297-18-3
eBook ISBN: 978-1-944297-19-0

Library of Congress Number: 2017935631

Designed and Formatted in the United States of America

MIX
Paper from
responsible sources
FSC® C011935

Contents

Introduction

"I'm thinking of writing a book of math jokes," I said to my wife.

She was long past the point of rolling her eyes at my ridiculous ideas. Instead, she was practical. "Do you really have enough jokes to fill a book?"

"I think so," I said. "I've got a file with over 400 jokes."

"No kidding?" she replied, somewhat surprised by my response.

"No kidding," I said. "And some of them are actually funny."

More than six years ago, those 400 jokes became *Math Jokes 4 Mathy Folks*, which has since sold more than 20,000 copies. While those sales numbers pale in comparison with *Harry Potter* and *War and Peace*, they have far exceeded my expectations. If you're one of the folks who purchased that first collection, thank you.

As a result of the success of *MJ4MF*, I've gotten to do a lot of fun things. I've performed an hour of stand-up comedy — with nothing but math jokes — in North Carolina, Virginia, and Connecticut. I was interviewed by Red Symons on ABC Radio Melbourne. I was even asked to deliver a webinar on the benefits of using humor in the math classroom. Who knew that one little book would singlehandedly consume the entirety of my 15 minutes of fame?

At one conference, I was given the dread penultimate time slot on the last day of the program, just before the closing session. When I asked the program chair why I was given such a terrible slot, he replied, "Because we figured people would stick around to hear you tell math jokes." That's quite a compliment. An even bigger compliment was the standing-room only crowd that filled the room with a queue of others waiting in the hallway.

Sorry, I don't mean to brag. I only mention these experiences because they've confirmed for me that math teachers and mathematicians laugh a lot more than most people would suspect, and nowhere is humor more necessary than in the math classroom.

But the most fun part of this ride? I've been inundated with math jokes from across the globe. Some arrived via email, many were posted to my blog, quite a few were relayed in conversation at math conferences, and one even arrived by snail mail. Like it or not, my inbox became a de facto storage location for overlooked and neglected math jokes.

When the dust settled, I found that I had another file with over 400 jokes in it.

"I'm thinking of writing another book of math jokes," I told my wife.

"I think you should," she said.

G. P. V.
May 2017

What happened in the binary race?

> Zero won.

Why is it impossible for a human arm to be exactly 12 inches long?

> Because then it would be a foot.

How do you make one disappear?

> Add a *g*, and it's *gone*.

What has 100 legs but can't walk?

> 50 pairs of pants.

What's the difference between a new penny and an old quarter?

> 24 cents.

If you had 5 apples in one hand and 7 apples in the other hand, what would you have?

> Very large hands.

What's one-fifth of a foot?

> A toe.

What's the range of log $(x - 2)$?

> $(2, \infty)$, and beyond!

If you choose an answer to this question at random, what is the probability that you will be correct?

- a) 25%
- b) 50%
- c) 60%
- d) 25%

A dog is at one end of a log;
At the opposite end is a frog.
Eight feet from the frog
And fifteen from the dog
Is a right angle. How long is the log?

> 17 feet

There were 99 people on a boat. The boat flipped over. How many people are left?

66!

If one man can wash a stack of dishes in an hour, how many stacks of dishes can four men wash in four hours?

None. They'll all sit down together and watch football on television.

You come to a fork in the road. One fork leads to the City of Truth, and the other leads to the City of Deceit. You can ask the person stationed at the fork in the road one yes-or-no question to find the City of Truth. If the person is from the City of Truth, he will answer your question honestly; if he is from the City of Deceit, he will answer your question dishonestly. What question should you ask?

"Did you know they're serving free beer in the City of Truth?" The truth-teller will say, "No!" and run to get a beer. The liar will say "Yes!" and run to get a beer. Either way, follow him.

If you can buy eight eggs for 26 cents, how many can you buy for a penny and a quarter?

Twenty-six.

What is $(108 - 12 \times 9) + (9 \times 2 - 18) + (49 - 7^2)$
$+ (64 - 16 \times 4) + (121 - 11 \times 11)$?

A lot of work for nothing!

What's the ratio of an octagon's perimeter to its diameter?

Octopi.

7, 8, 9

*The best-known math joke in the history of the world is, "Why is 6 afraid of 7?" And the punch line, of course, is "Because 7 8 9!" As such, it is also the math joke that has spawned the greatest number of variations. Several are included below, the most impressive being the Turkish version with the word **yedi**, which is the Turkish word for both **seven** and **ate**.*

Why is 10 afraid of 7?

Because 7 8 9.

How did 9 get revenge on 7?

9 8 7!

Why don't jokes work in base 8?

Because 7 10 11.

Why do Canadians prefer jokes in hexadecimal?

Because 7 8 9 A.

Why is 6 afraid of 7?

Because 7 is a known six offender.

Why is 6 afraid of 7?

> He's playing craps and his point is 10.

Why is 5 (bes) afraid of 6 (alti)?

> Because 6 (alti) 7 (yedi) 8 (sekiz).

Why is ε (epsilon) afraid of θ (theta)?

> Because ζ (zeta) η (eta) θ (theta).

Why is 6 afraid of 7?

> It isn't. Numbers are not sentient and therefore are incapable of feeling fear.

Why Windows 10?

> Because Windows 7 8 9.

Why is Yoda afraid of 7?

> Because 6 7 8.

In the Classroom

A student calls his school and says, "My son injured his wrist last night, so he wasn't able to complete his math homework."

The school secretary asks, "Who is this?"

The student responds, "This is my father speaking!"

When asked if she missed math class yesterday, Alissa replied, "Not at all!"

When the teacher told the class that they would have a test tomorrow, rain or shine, one student noted, "Great! It's snowing!"

When the student told the teacher that he didn't deserve a zero on the test, she replied, "I agree, but that's the lowest score I'm allowed to give you."

When asked if he learned a lot in math class today, Julian said, "Apparently not! I have to go back tomorrow."

The teacher told the class, "We will have only a half-day of school this morning." The students cheered. She then told them, "We will have the other half this afternoon!"

To get a good grade in geometry, you have to know all the angles.

Knowledge is power, and power corrupts. So study hard, and be evil!

Math teachers don't suffer from insanity. They enjoy every minute of it.

A rubber band pistol was confiscated from a student in algebra class, because it was a weapon of math disruption.

Why didn't the math class have any desks?
    They didn't need them. They had times tables.

When I got an F in algebra, my mom was really mad and couldn't believe that I failed. But I told her, "That's not what that means. That's an F in algebra. It's a variable. We don't know what it means. It *could* mean I failed, but it probably just means I'm fantastic."

I prayed for a good grade in math class, but I know prayers don't work that way. So, I cheated on my math test, and I prayed for forgiveness.

January   **Class Roster**

MJ4MF High	Vennebush		Room 1729		
	M	T	W	T	F
Matt Amatics					
Cal Culator					
Vin Culum					
Cal Culus					
Rose Curve					
Polly Gon					
Al Gorithm					
Polly Hedron					
Al Jabra					
Ella Ment					
Perry Meter					
Polly Nomial					
Hy Perbola					
Lisa Perbound					
M. T. Set					
May Trix					
Al T. Tude					
Norm Ull					

A young boy came home from school in tears.

"What's the matter?" asked his mother.

"We were doing math in school today," he said.

"And...?"

"And the teacher said either I couldn't count, or I was stupid, or all three!"

A teacher poses a problem to her class. "If a mail carrier runs at 12 kilometers per hour, a dog runs at 15 kilometers per hour, and the mailman has a 50-meter head start, how long will it take the dog to catch the mail carrier? Solve the problem graphically." When a student says that he can't solve the problem, the teacher asks, "Why not?"

"I can't draw dogs."

Why did the student wear glasses in math class?

Because it helps to improve division.

A student asks, "What's infinity?" and the teacher tells her to think of a number.

"Okay, I've got one," says the student.

The teacher replies, "Good. That's not it."

A math student is pestered by a classmate who wants to copy her homework. The student hesitates not only because she thinks it's wrong, but she's also afraid of getting caught.

Her classmate calms her down. "Don't worry, no one will be able to tell. I'll change the names of all the constants and variables: a to b, x to y, and so on."

She's not convinced, but she wants to be left alone, so she agrees and hands her assignment to her classmate. After the deadline, she asks, "Did you really change the names of all the variables?"

"Of course!" the classmate replies. "What you called a function f, I called it g. When you called a variable x, I renamed it to y. And when you were writing about the log of $x + 1$, I called it the timber of $x + 1$..."

When asked to try harder, the math student told her teacher that she gives 110% effort every week:

  8% on Monday
21% on Tuesday
38% on Wednesday
27% on Thursday
16% on Friday

A computer science student is told by his mother to set the table.

"To what?" he replies.

An excited son says, "I got 100% in math class today!"

"That's great!" his mom replies. "On what?"

The son says, "50% on my homework, and 50% on my quiz!"

A math teacher was driving past his student's house. The student was digging in the mud. The teacher stopped and asked why. "Because on the radio, they said it rained an inch and three-quarters last night, so I'm looking for the three quarters!"

What will you find in the back of a probability textbook?

Odds.

Marian was asked for the sum of 4 + 4. She replied, "8."

"Very good," said her teacher. "You may take 8 pieces of candy from the candy jar."

"If I had known that," Marian responded, "I would have said 100!"

"I can't use this calculator," said the student to his teacher. "It never does what I want it to. It only does what I tell it to."

When asked for the circumference of a circle, the pirate replied, "2π, Arrr!"

William was not proud of his report card. He brought home an F in English and a D– in math. His father signed an X on the line for the parent signature.

"What'd you do that for?" William asked.

"I don't want your teacher to know that you were raised by people who can read and write."

Summer school has been good for me. I've saved a lot on sunscreen.

The teacher asked Manny if he knew his numbers.
"Yes," he said. "I do. My father taught me."

"Good. What comes after three?"

"Four," answered the boy.

"What comes after six?"

"Seven."

"Excellent," said the teacher. "Your dad did a good job. And what comes after ten?"

"Jack," said Manny.

The math teacher saw that Quinn wasn't paying attention. She said, "Quinn! What are 28 and 17?"

Quinn replied, "CBS and Cartoon Network."

Excuses for Not Doing Your Math Homework

- I had a constant amount of homework. I tried to derive its purpose, but I got nothing.

- I could only get arbitrarily close to my textbook, but I could never reach it.

- I am sure that I put it inside my Klein Bottle last night, but this morning I couldn't find it.

- I locked it in my trunk, but a four-dimensional dog got in and ate it.

- I wanted to, but I couldn't find its Gödel Number.

- I did some of it. The part I have left to do is 0.9999...

- I didn't know whether i is the square root of –1 or i am the square root of –1.

- I accidentally divided by 0, and my paper burst into flames.

- Someone already published it, so I didn't bother to write it.

- I have a solar calculator, but it was cloudy yesterday.

- There wasn't enough room to write it in the margin.

Melania said, "Proofs are so boring!"

Her geometry teacher quickly replied, "Well, that's a given."

Why did the child eat his homework?

> Because his teacher said it was a piece of cake.

The teacher asked, "If you had one dollar and you asked your father for another, how many dollars would you have?"

The student replied, "One dollar."

"Young lady," said the teacher, "you don't know your arithmetic."

The student replied, "And you don't know my father!"

An abacus can always be counted on.

The tutor asked, "If I had five coconuts and I gave you three, how many would I have left?"

The tutee responded, "I don't know. In school, we do arithmetic with apples and oranges."

The teacher asked Alex, "Do you know what they call people who keep talking when people are no longer interested?"

"Math teachers?"

The teacher gave an example of an inverse proportion. "If it takes 6 days for 2 men to finish a task, how long will it take 3 men to complete the same task? The number of men needed is inversely proportional to the number of days required. Consequently, 3 men will be able to complete the task in 6 × 2/3 = 4 days."

A student responds, "Oh, I get it! I think I've got a real-life application of this. If it takes 6 hours for 2 men to hike to the top of a hill, then it will only take 4 hours for 3 men to hike to the top of the hill!"

Higher Education

To steal ideas from one person is plagiarism. To steal from many is research.

Good teachers borrow. Great teachers steal.

Education is when you read the fine print. Experience is what you get when you don't.

How do you get a grad student to laugh on Thursday?

Tell him a joke on Monday.

Did you hear about the math professor who locked her keys in her car?

She had to break a window to get her graduate assistant out.

What should you do when a math PhD comes to your door?

Pay him, and take your pizza.

What's the difference between a grad student and a savings bond?

A savings bond eventually matures.

A grad student walks into the math department and sees three undergraduates. One of them is holding a board vertically, the second is steadying a chair on a desk, and the third is standing on the chair. The third student has one end of a measuring tape, and the first student is holding the other end. The grad student asks, "What are you doing?"

The undergraduates answer, "We're trying to measure this board."

The grad student says, "Why not put it on the floor and measure it?"

The undergraduates answer, "We already know its length! We want to know its height."

The failing math student went to the professor's office to get some help. When he arrived, several students were ahead of him, so he waited patiently for his turn. When he finally went in, he asked his question, and the professor spent the better part of an hour trying various explanations, but nothing worked. The student was clearly frustrated.

"Well," said the professor. "I suppose after you graduate, you'll be waiting for me to die so you can spit on my grave."

"Oh, no," said the student. "After I graduate, I ain't never gonna stand in line again!"

What's your daughter going to be when she graduates from college?

A senior citizen.

A chemistry major, an economics major, and a math major are urinating in a bathroom.

The chemistry major finishes, then washes his hands thoroughly using lots of soap and water, and says, "In the chemistry department, they teach us to be clean."

The economics major finishes, then washes his hands with a very small amount of soap and water, and says, "In the economics department, they teach us how to conserve resources."

The math major finishes and walks right towards the door. On his way out, he says, "In the math department, they teach us not to piss on our hands."

After all three have left, a religious studies major walks into the bathroom, washes his hands thoroughly, and then proceeds to the urinal. To no one in particular, he says, "In our department, they teach us to wash our hands before handling sacred objects."

The failing student showed up to the math professor's office with a hundred-dollar bottle of scotch. The professor objected, "I'm sorry, taking a gift from a student would be unethical."

The student said, "I understand. But what if I sell it to you for $10?"

The math professor thought for a moment. "At that price, I'll take a whole case!"

A student asked his logic professor, "Ma'am, did I pass or fail the exam?"

The professor replied, "Yes!"

A student at a state university was looking at scores from the midterm exam that had been posted on a wall in the math building. She noticed that she had the lowest score. The student who received the second-lowest score was making fun of her and asked, "How's it feel to have the lowest score?"

She replied, "Why don't you see for yourself?" and walked away. The next day, she dropped the course.

A professor called a failing student into his office. "I've noticed," he began, "that every time there's a big home game, you miss class and say you have to take your aunt to the doctor."

"My goodness, you're right!" said the student. "You don't suppose she's been faking it, do you?"

A math professor, his student, an old lady, and a beautiful young woman find themselves together on a train. The train passes through a tunnel, and in the darkness a loud slap is heard. When they exit the tunnel, they see that the professor has a red, five-finger mark on his cheek.

The old lady thinks, "That guy must have groped the young woman in the dark, and she slapped him."

The blonde thinks, "That student must have tried to grope me in the dark and mistakenly groped the old lady, so she slapped him."

The professor thinks, "Perhaps my student groped the blonde in the dark, and she mistakenly slapped me instead of him."

The student thinks, "That'll teach that son-of-a-bitch for giving me a failing grade on my mid-term!"

A poor grad student started counterfeiting money. He proudly showed his friend a seventeen-dollar bill he had made.

"That's great," said his friend, "but a seventeen-dollar bill is useless."

"No, it's not!" he insisted, then stormed down to the corner store. He was smiling when he returned five minutes later. "See?" he said, "I asked the clerk for change, and he gave me two sevens and a three!"

I've been asked to say a couple of words about Professor Thompson. How about *unfair* and *absent-minded*?

The chair of the math department walked into the President's office and demanded a raise. "But you're already the highest paid member of the faculty," the President insisted.

"Maybe so, but you don't know what I have to deal with," she said. "Watch this." She stepped into the hallway, grabbed one of her graduate assistants, and said, "Go to my office and see if I'm there."

The grad student returned five minutes later. "No, ma'am, you're not there," he said.

"I see what you mean," said the President. "He should've called first."

My statistics professor said that if we didn't like our exam results, we just needed to change our level of confidence.

During a physics lecture, the professor wrote the equation $E = h\,v$ on the board. He then asked, "What is v?"

"Planck's constant."

"Good. And what is h?"

"The length of the plank."

When asked what kinds of problems would be on the final, the professor replied, "Just study the old tests. The problems will be the same, but the numbers will be different. Although not all the numbers will be different. Planck's constant will be the same, π will be the same, ..."

Another professor, when asked how many problems would be on the final, turned to the student and replied, "I suspect you'll have lots of problems on the final."

A professor giving a lecture covered several blackboards with expressions full of Bessel functions. She then remembered that there were many undergraduates in the room. Feeling slight remorse that perhaps she was talking over their heads, she turned around and asked if anyone had never seen a Bessel function before. The audience was silent for a few seconds, but then one intrepid student raised his hand and admitted that he hadn't. The professor nodded with apparent comprehension. Without hesitation, she turned around, pointed to the blackboard, said, "Well, there's one now," and continued her talk.

Professions

A physician provides an analysis of a complex illness, but a statistician makes you ill with complex analysis.

An actuary is a person who measures with a micrometer, marks with chalk, and cuts with an axe.

An actuary is a numbers nut who reads very thick books with tiny, tiny print and enjoys the footnotes more than the text.

A statistician is an accountant who doesn't play golf.

Mathematicians like to have fun... but only if no one is watching.

Mathematicians are flexible: they are either correct, or they can prove it to be so.

An actuary is a math geek who wanted to be an accountant but didn't have the personality.

An actuary is someone who'd rather be completely wrong than approximately right.

A quant, when asked what time it is, will tell you how to build a watch.

An accountant, a lawyer, and an actuary are walking down the street when a woman accidentally drops a number of coins from her pocket onto the sidewalk. The accountant glances at the coins, totals their value, and advises the woman on how much she lost. The lawyer ignores the coins and starts searching the sidewalk for dollar bills. And the actuary uses the total value of the lost coins to project how much is still left in the woman's pocket.

A mathematician asked her colleague, "So why did you become a mathematician?"

She replied, "I don't like working with numbers."

The physicist asked the mathematician, "Why did the chicken cross the road?"

The mathematician pondered a while and then replied, "I have a solution, but it only works for a spherical chicken in a vacuum."

The electrical engineer's daughter got quite a shock while playing with an outlet. The engineer had to ground her.

An applied mathematician and a pure mathematician pull into a parking spot. The applied mathematician locked the door, and both of them walked away. A bit later, he said to the pure mathematician, "Uh-oh. I dropped my key somewhere along the way." She returned to the car along the same path, looking for her key. When she found it, she looked up to find that the pure mathematician was searching at the other end of the parking lot. "What are you doing?" asked the applied mathematician. "I lost my key over there. Why would you look over here?" The pure mathematician replied, "There's better light over here."

What do you call an accountant with a sense of humor?

Part qualified.

A statistician and an actuary walked into a bar. The statistician yelled, "Ouch!" The actuary replied, "Watch out!"

After taking a course in heredity, a statistician concluded that if your parents didn't have any children, the probability is very high that you won't, either.

A government research firm, upon collecting hundreds of obituaries, concluded that on any given day, people die in alphabetical order.

"Given that you have absolutely no experience as a statistician," said the personnel director, "don't you think you're requesting an awfully high salary?"

"Not really," the candidate said. "Think how much harder it's going to be for me to do the work if I don't know anything about it."

What does a mathematician say when asked whether she would like the window open or closed?

"Yes."

The logician and his wife stayed in a hotel for one night and received a bill for $300. "Three hundred dollars!" he protested. "For what?"

"Room and board," the hotel manager explained.

"But we didn't eat here."

The manager said, "We offer breakfast, lunch, and dinner in the dining room. If you didn't take advantage of it, that's your fault."

The logician handed the manager $100. "Here," he said. "That's to cover the room. I'm charging you $200 for sleeping with my wife."

The manager said, "But I never touched your wife!"

"Oh, really? Because she was waiting for you in our room. If you didn't take advantage of it, that's your fault."

A lawyer and a mathematician were sitting next to each other on a chartered fishing boat. The lawyer said, "I'm here because my house was destroyed by a fire, and the insurance company paid for everything."

"What a coincidence!" said the mathematician. "My house was destroyed by a flood, and my insurance company paid for everything, too."

"Really?" asked the lawyer. "How on Earth did you start a flood?"

A professor is on an airplane.

"Would you like dinner?" the flight attendant asks.

"What are my choices?"

"Yes or no."

Four surgeons were discussing their work. The first said, "I think accountants make the best patients. Everything inside is numbered."

"Librarians are better," said the second. "Their organs are alphabetized."

The third said, "I prefer electricians. They're color-coded."

"I like to operate on statisticians," the fourth said. "They're heartless and gutless, and their heads are interchangeable with their asses."

Everyone knows that if a mathematician had to choose between solving a difficult story problem and catching a fly ball, he would surely solve the problem without thinking twice about whether the Infield Fly Rule was in effect.

A consulting company needed to hire a quantitative type, and they were interviewing a pure mathematician, an engineer, and an applied mathematician. All of the interviewees were male, so the company gave them the following test: a beautiful woman was lounging on a couch at the end of the hallway. An administrative assistant explained, "You can go half the distance to the woman at a time. When you reach the woman, you may kiss her."

The pure mathematician said, "It's impossible to reach the woman in a finite number of iterations," and he withdrew his name from consideration.

The engineer bounded halfway down the hall, then halfway again, and so on. After several bounds, he declared that he was well within an acceptable tolerance, wrapped his arms around the beautiful woman, and kissed her.

The applied mathematician did not move at all. Instead, he grabbed the assistant and kissed her.

"What are you doing?" she asked.

"I'm an applied mathematician. You gave me a problem I couldn't solve, so I changed the problem!"

When a scientist claimed that 95% of people exposed to a particular strain of bacteria are likely to get sick, a newspaper reported, "This just in — scientists not 100% certain that this strain poses a danger to human health."

A researcher tried jalapenos on a stomach ulcer patient, and the ulcer went away. The researcher published an article "Jalapenos Cure Stomach Ulcers." The next patient subjected to the same treatment died. The researcher published a follow-up article, "More Detailed Study Reveals That Jalapenos Cure 50% Of Stomach Ulcers."

If you understand it and can prove it, then send your paper to a journal of mathematics.

If you understand it but can't prove it, then send it to a journal of physics.

If you can't understand it but can prove it, then send it to an journal of economics.

If you can neither understand it nor prove it, then send it to a journal of psychology.

If it attempts to make something important out of something trivial, then send it to a journal of education.

If it attempts to make something trivial out of something important, send it to a journal of metaphysics.

Statistics in the hands of an engineer are like lampposts to a drunk — they're used more for support than illumination.

An optimist says, "The glass is half full."

A pessimist says, "The glass is half empty."

A set theorist says, "The amount of water hasn't changed cardinality. It still has cardinality $\aleph_1$."

A graph theorist says, "The water is now self-complementary."

An applied mathematician says, "The temperature and pressure must have risen dramatically."

A topologist says, "The water hasn't changed significantly."

An algebraist says, "The water is completely the same, mod 2."

An analyst says, "It's undergone a contraction mapping."

A combinatorist says, "The task of choosing an arbitrary water molecule has been reduced by a subtask of two possibilities."

A consulting mathematician says, "Hey, I ordered coffee!"

Did you hear about the middle school math teacher who became a dentist?

Her specialty is square root canals.

Did you hear about the geometrician who became a taxidermist?

His specialty is furrier (Fourier) transforms.

Did you hear about the engineer who was so dull that the other engineers actually noticed?

"Can you help me out?" said the beggar to the economist who was passing by. "I haven't eaten in a week."

"I'm sorry to hear that," said the economist, "but how does that compare with the same period last year?"

A shoe seller meets a mathematician and complains that he doesn't know how many shoes to stock in his store. "No problem," says the mathematician. "There's a simple equation for that," and he proceeds to show him the Gaussian normal distribution.

The shoe seller stares at the equation for quite some time and then asks about one of the symbols.

"That's the Greek letter π," explains the mathematician.

"What is π?"

"It's the ratio between the circumference and the diameter of a circle."

The shoe seller thinks about this for a moment then finally replies, "What the hell does a circle have to do with shoes?"

St. Peter and a large crowd are waiting at the Pearly Gates when an analytical consultant arrives. "Congratulations!" says St. Peter. "You're the oldest person to ever come through these gates!"

"How can that be?" asks the consultant. "I was only 45 when I died."

"Really?" asks St. Peter. "Based on your billable hours, we thought you were at least 130!"

An actuary, an underwriter, and an insurance salesperson are riding in a car. The salesperson has his foot on the gas, the underwriter has her foot on the brake, and the actuary is looking out the back window telling them where to go.

I once told a mathematician to go to the end of the line. He came back five minutes later and said he couldn't, because someone was already there.

When a statistician was asked why she recommends selling life insurance policies to 98-year olds, she replied, "According to my research, very few of them die each year."

Why did the statistician want to be buried in Israel?

The probability of resurrection is better there.

An actuary sees someone about to dive into an empty pool. He whispers, "Stop, there's no water." The person dives and lands on the bottom of the pool. The actuary shouts, "Told you!"

A statistician is walking down a corridor when she feels a pain in her chest. Immediately, she runs to the stairwell and hurls herself down the stairs. Her friend, visiting her in the hospital, asks why she did it. The statistician replies, "Having a heart attack while falling down the stairs is much less likely than just having a heart attack."

A mathematician and a statistician are watching the 11 o'clock news. A story comes on involving a man on a window ledge threatening to jump. The statistician says, "I'll bet you $50 he doesn't jump."

The mathematician says, "I'll take that bet."

A few minutes later, they see that the guy jumps. As the statistician reaches for his wallet, the mathematician says, "Keep your money. This wasn't fair. I saw the 6 o'clock news."

The statistician responds, "So did I. I just never thought it would happen twice."

A mathematician owns several hens, and his annoying, physicist neighbor watches him collect the eggs every morning. One day, a hen escapes and lays an egg in the physicist's yard. The mathematician sees this, and a dispute ensues over whose egg it is. After much arguing, the mathematician finally suggests a contest to settle the matter. "We'll kick each other where it hurts, and whoever takes less time to get up wins the egg."

The physicist agrees. The mathematician goes inside, puts on his steel-toed boots, takes a run at the physicist, and swings his leg as hard as he can. The engineer collapses and lays on the ground for 45 minutes. He finally stands up and says, "Okay, now it's my turn."

"Nah," says the mathematician. "You can keep the egg."

A statistician arrived at a soda machine a few moments before a mathematician. The statistician inserted 50¢, studied the machine, pressed the Pepsi button, and then placed the can of Pepsi on the counter after it fell to the bottom. She then inserted a dollar, studied the machine again, pressed the Dr Pepper button, and again placed the can on the counter after it fell. She took the 50¢ change from the previous purchase, inserted it, selected Mountain Dew, and once again placed the can on the counter. The mathematician, annoyed at watching this, asked, "Are you done yet?"

The statistician indignantly replied, "Well, no. I'm still winning!"

When a research mathematician enters the room for a job interview with a dog and a cow, the stunned interviewer asks, "I'm sorry, ma'am, but what do you think you're doing?"

The woman replies, "These are my colleagues, and they are very special animals."

"How so?"

"They're knot theorists. And if you hire me, then you'll get all three of us for one salary."

The interviewer, skeptical, says, "I've met a number of mathematicians who were animals, but I've never met an animal that was a mathematician."

"Well, I'll prove it. Ask them anything about mathematics that you like."

So the interviewer asks the dog, "Name a knot invariant."

"Arf," barks the dog.

The interviewer scowls. He turns to the cow and asks, "What is the integrating factor of an ordinary differential equation?"

The cow says, "Mu."

The interviewer turns to the woman and says, "Just what are you trying to pull?" He asks her to leave and take the animals with her.

Outside, the dog turns to the woman and asks, "Should I have said the Jones polynomial instead?"

Two applied mathematicians were sitting in a movie theater, and a pure mathematician sat down next to them along the aisle. During the previews, the pure mathematician removed his shoes and started to relax. Just then, one of the applied mathematicians said, "I think I'd like a soda."

"No problem," said the pure mathematician. "Let me get it for you." While he was gone, one of the applied mathematicians picked up one of his shoes and spat in it.

When the pure mathematician returned, the other applied mathematician said, "Ya know, I think I'd like a soda, too." Again, the pure mathematician offered to get it, and while he was gone, the applied mathematicians spat in his other shoe. He returned with the second soda, and they sat quietly through the movie. As the credits started to roll, the pure mathematician slipped his shoes back on, and he realized immediately what had happened.

"How long must this go on?" he asked. "This fighting between our professions? This hatred? This animosity? This spitting in shoes and pissing in sodas?"

Why did the engineer keep a can of lubricating oil in her top drawer?

> To oil the wheels of his chair; otherwise, they could squeak, and someone might notice she was there.

What is a statistician's preferred form of contraception?

> Talking about his job.

Three economists go to lunch. The waiter leaves a check for $26.40, and the economists decide to split it evenly. How much does each one pay?

> Nothing. Economists always round to the nearest million.

What does an engineer's spouse do to cure insomnia?

> Rolls over and says, "Tell me what you did at work today."

A farmer wants to improve the milk production of his cows so he brings in an engineer, a psychologist, and a statistician to analyze the problem.

The engineer says, "Well, if we make the stalls this big, add a loft, put more stalls over there, and run the pipes this way and that, then we can fit more cows in this building, thus increasing your milk production."

The psychologist says, "Well, if we paint the floor green and the walls and ceiling blue, we can trick the cows into thinking they're outside. They'll be happier, and happier cows produce more milk."

The statistician says, "Actually, I don't have an approach, but if you try the engineer's and psychologist's ideas, I can set up a simulation to tell you what you should have done in the first place. That is, if the cows are credible."

A marketing person was trying to convince an agent that a glass half full of water could be easily sold to the companies' clients. A nearby engineer overheard the conversation.

The marketer explains, "This glass contains water that is clear, refreshing, and satisfying. It's the best water on the market. Anyone could sell this."

The agent replies, "That glass is half empty. How can you expect me to sell that? No one can sell a glass that isn't full."

The engineer offers, "Personally, I think there's just way too much glass."

When you ask a pure mathematician a question that requires a one-sentence answer, she'll respond by telling you where to find the source material from which you can calculate the answer yourself, then proceed to describe the pros and cons for the various methods of calculation.

How can you tell the difference between a CPA and an actuary?

By which side of the bars they're on.

What do you call a statistician who graduated last in his class?

CPA.

What do the accountants at Enron, WorldCom, and Arthur Anderson have in common with the complex plane?

They all use imaginary numbers.

An engineer, a physicist, and a statistician are in a hotel when a fire starts. "Pour water on it!" cries the engineer.

"No, remove the oxygen!" says the physicist.

The statistician, seeing their disagreement, frantically runs around the hotel starting fires. "What the hell are you doing?" the other two ask.

"Creating a decent sample size."

Five cannibals are hired as engineers at a defense company. The boss welcomes them, tells them they have complete access to the cafeteria, but asks them not to bother the other employees. Four weeks later, the boss congratulates them for their hard work, but she also says that the janitor is missing. "Do any of you know what happened to him?" the boss asks. None of them says anything, and the boss leaves.

When the boss is out of earshot, one of the cannibals says, "Okay, which of you idiots ate the janitor?" Meekly, one of them raises his hand. "You, idiot!" shouts the first. "For a month, we've been eating accountants, statisticians, mathematicians, engineers, project managers, and supervisors, and no one noticed! But you had to go and eat the janitor!"

What's the difference between a mathematician and a physicist?

The mathematician thinks there is only one straight line that passes through two points; the physicist, however, needs more data.

Statisticians and diapers have one thing in common — they should both be changed regularly, and for the same reason.

You might be a mathematician if you think fog is a composition of functions.

What do you call a mathematician who's been standing out in the cold longer than any other member of her department?

A number theorist.

What's the difference between math professors and actuaries?

Actuaries know they're boring.

How can you be sure that a statistical analyst is really dead?

Hold out a check.

Light Bulb

How many math consultants does it take to change
a light bulb?

> Three. One to change it, and the others to confuse
> the issue.

How many extroverted mathematicians does it take
to screw in a light bulb?

> Both of them.

How many social scientists does it take to change
a light bulb?

> None. They're too busy trying to determine the
> reasons why the last bulb went out.

How many textbook authors does it take to change
a light bulb?

> The solution to this question is left as an exercise
> for the reader.

How many engineers does it take to change a light bulb?

> Unknown. They're still waiting on a part.

How many mathematicians working in corporate settings does it take to change a light bulb?

None. Upper management prefers to leave them in the dark.

How many math department faculty does it take to screw in a light bulb?

Two. A professor with tenure presents the proposal to the dean, and an adjunct does all the work.

How many topologists does it take to change a light bulb?

None. They'd rather knot.

How many tenure-track professors does it take to change a light bulb?

Seven. One to change the bulb, and six to write the proposal for the research grant.

How many analysts does it take to change a light bulb?

Have any of our competitors changed bulbs yet?

How many statisticians does it take to change a light bulb?

How many do you want it to take?

How many engineers does it take to change a light bulb?

Just one, so long as she has the instruction manual.

How many engineers does it take to change a light bulb?

> Five. One to screw it in, and four to estimate the length of its life before being screwed in.

How many help-desk technicians does it take to change a light bulb?

> None. Just turn the light off, turn it back on again, and see what happens.

How many algebra teachers does it take to change a light bulb?

> x^0.

How many webmasters does it take to change a light bulb?

> 404.

How many statisticians does it take to change a light bulb?

> On average, or do you want the whole distribution?

How many famous Italian mathematicians does it take to change a light bulb?

> 1, 1, 2, 3, 5, 8, 13, 21, ...

How many actuaries does it take to change a light bulb?

What the hell is a light bulb? That wasn't on any of the exams!

How many accountants does it take to find the present value of an annuity?

Three. One to determine the amount of each payment, one to figure out the account into which the answer should be placed, and one to ask an actuary how to calculate it.

How many mathematicians does it take to change a light bulb?

Just one. She gives it to three physicists, thus reducing it to a problem that has already been solved.

How many actuaries does it take to change a light bulb?

How many did it take last year?

How many members of a certain demographic group does it take to perform a specified task?

$n + 1$. One to perform the task, and n others to act in a manner stereotypical of the group.

Q & A

How is reading a book of math jokes like hitting your head with a ball-peen hammer?

Both feel better when you stop.

Why didn't the two 4's feel like dinner?

Because they already 8.

Did you hear about the Irishman who liked to multiply by two?

He loved Dublin.

What did the Venn diagram say to infinity?

"Eat something, dude!"

What did the trig teacher say to the triangles?

"You're all right."

How much did the pirate pay to have his ears pierced?

A buccaneer!

What has eight legs and eight eyes?
> Eight pirates.

What grade did the pirate get in math class?
> High C's.

How many insects inhabit an apartment?
> Ten ants.

What does a mathematician yell when he's golfing?
> "2 + 2!"

What is the most military day of the year?
> March 4th.

What do you get if you cross a math teacher and a clock?
> Arithma-ticks.

What did the square say to the old circle?
> "Been 'round long?"

What's between 7 and 8?
> The word *and*.

What did the dollar say to four quarters?

"You've changed!"

Did you hear about the new calculator for the mathematically challenged?

It's a giant hand with 10,000 fingers.

What did the boxer do to the calculator?

He punched some buttons.

What do you call falling out of plane without a parachute?

Jumping to a conclusion.

What do you call a witty person at a math department social event?

Lost.

What do you call a smiling, sober, courteous person at a math department social event?

The caterer.

What do you call a mathematician who is talking to someone?

Popular.

How does an economist liven up a party?
　　She leaves.

How does an accountant liven up a party?
　　He brings an economist.

What's the difference between a dead math teacher on the road and a dead cat on the road?
　　There are skid marks near the cat.

Why did the statistician cross the interstate?
　　To analyze data on the other side of the median.

y?
　　yo?

Which polygon is also a card trick?
　　Decagon.

What did the 8 say to infinity?
　　"Rise and shine, buddy!"

What's the difference between the radius and the diameter?
　　The radius.

How good are you at algebra?
"Vary able."

Which animals are the most proficient at math?

- Rabbits, because they multiply.
- Amoebae, because they divide.
- Snakes, because they're adders.
- Beavers, because they work with natural logs.
- Flamingoes, because they balance.

How is simplifying a fraction like powdering your nose?
Both improve the appearance without changing the value.

Why didn't the Romans find algebra challenging?
Because X always equals 10.

Why is addition by hand so difficult?
Because of how many things you have to carry.

What's the difference between a math professor and a terrorist?
You can negotiate with a terrorist.

Where does a one-armed man shop?
At a second-hand store.

What's the difference between a mathematician and the deceased person at a funeral?

> The deceased person is wearing a clean shirt.

Why was 1/5 sent to a counselor?

> Because he was two-tenths (too tense).

How is the moon like a dollar?

> Both have four quarters.

What occurs once in a minute, twice in a week, but only once in a year?

> The letter *e*.

How many eggs can you put in an empty basket?

> Just one. Then it isn't empty anymore.

What coin doubles in value when half is taken away?

> A half dollar.

When things go wrong, what can you always count on?

> Your fingers.

What goes up and never comes down?

> Your age.

What is the most used tool in a math class?
    Multi-pliers.

What do you get when you cross an old acquaintance with an abacus?
    A friend you can count on.

Why wouldn't the pizza box fit in the recycling can?
    It's putting a square peg in a round hole.

How can you get straight A's?
    Use a ruler.

What did the complementary angle say to the isosceles triangle?
    "Nice legs!"

What did the circle say to the tangent line?
    "Stop touching me!"

Why wasn't the right triangle's loan approved?
    Because tangent wouldn't cosine.

What is the ratio of the circumference of a bowl of ice cream to its diameter?

Pi a la mode.

Did you hear about the murderous mathematician?

He went on a killing spree with a pair of axes.

What is half of 8?

Either 3 or 0, depending on whether you divide it vertically or horizontally.

What do you get when you cross the Godfather with a math professor?

An offer you can't understand.

A math major got a 2400 on the SAT. An engineering major got a 2360 on the SAT. What did the liberal arts major get on the SAT?

Drool.

What do you call a beautiful woman on the arm of a math graduate student?

A tattoo.

What do you call a guy who hangs out with mathematicians?

A grad student.

What's a math graduate student without a girlfriend?

Homeless.

What did the genie say to the mathematician who rubbed his lamp?

"I've already squared the circle and trisected an angle. Now, what's your third wish?"

Which American highway is related to the length of the vector (7,4,1)?

Root 66.

What's the difference between lottery players and actuaries?

Lottery players sometimes get the numbers correct, and actuaries get a large amount of money they didn't earn.

What is $PA + PN + LA + LN$?

A $(P + L)(A + N)$ that's been FOILed.

Two cats sit on a sloping roof. One is black, the other is white. Which one falls off first?

The one with the lesser μ.

Why did the tachyon cross the road?

Because it was already there!

Why don't members of the Ku Klux Klan study Calculus?
Because they don't like to integrate.

What do you call it when you're trying to prove that a map is injective, but you just can't do it?
Monic fail.

What does a mathematician present to her fiancé when she wants to propose?
A polynomial ring.

Why did the chicken cross the North Pole?
He didn't want to waste time walking across the R^2 plane.

What kind of maps should you take with you on car trips?
Automorphisms.

Where does a pirate graph complex numbers?
Arr-gand plane!

Why can fish from the United States enter Canadian waters without a passport?
It's allowed by the Law of Aquatic Reciprocity!

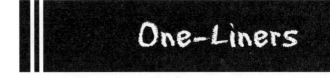
One-Liners

I told ten puns to friends, with the hope that at least one would make them laugh. Unfortunately, no pun in ten did.

If you get depressed when you think about how dumb the average person is, then you'll likely be horrified when you realize that half the population is even dumber.

Having gone to school doesn't make you a teacher any more than standing in a garage makes you a car.

Half the population is below median intelligence, but well over half the population is above average. This is due to the fact that there is a limit to human intelligence, but no limit to human stupidity.

If you don't think random sampling works, the next time you go for a blood test, tell the nurse to take it all.

I thought it was a great idea to name our kid Pi... until the first time he misbehaved, and I had to call him by his full name.

The midget fortune-teller who escaped from prison was a small medium at large.

A news show reported that a new largest prime number has been found, and it is four times as large as the previous record.

Women should not have children after 35. Really, 35 children should be plenty for anyone.

If you laid all the statisticians in the world end to end, they still wouldn't reach agreement.

If all the people who fall asleep in church were laid end to end, they'd be a lot more comfortable.

I'm reading a great book on anti-gravity. I just can't put it down!

Two barcodes go to a shady optometrist. They sit and stare at a light for half an hour. One of them finally says, "Let's get out of here. I think this is a scan."

Two lines walk into a barcode. They hashed it out.

In life, trees grow roots. In math, roots split logs.

C programmers have been known to press "3" to get to the fourth floor.

There are over 25 times as many four-letter acronyms as there are three-letter acronyms.

Nearly half the population has a double-digit IQ.

The total intelligence of our planet is constant, but the population is increasing exponentially.

Never strike up a conversation with π. He'll just go on and on forever!

Five out of four people have trouble with fractions.

A recent report stated that one in four people has a mental illness. Now look at your three best friends. If they're okay, then it's you.

Natural numbers are better for your health.

I have a digital calculator. Every time I want to count, I use my fingers.

Though he pursued his studies relentlessly, they were never effectively overtaken.

Infinity is terrible. I mean, when's it gonna stop?

A recent report stated that Americans are geographically illiterate and financially ignorant. It's true! How many times have you heard someone say, "Where did all my money go?"

You have to stay in shape. My grandmother started walking 5 miles a day when she turned 60. Now she's 92, and we have no idea where she is.

I just flew on a supersonic jet. It flew at twice the speed of sound. I got home really fast, but I couldn't hear the movie until two hours after we landed.

The mathematician hit it big in Las Vegas. He drove there in a $12,000 car, and after two hours at the poker tables, he returned home in a $40,000 bus.

"I'm in a real hurry," said the diner. "How long to make me a three-minute egg?"

When I heard that it only costs $10 a year to support a child in India, I bought one-way tickets for my kids.

I bought one gallon of whole milk, because I couldn't afford 50 gallons of 2% milk.

Think of the biggest number you can. Now add 5. Then, imagine if you had that many doughnuts. Wow, that's 5 more than the biggest number you could come up with!

A man who says that marriage is a 50-50 proposition fails to understand women or ratios or both.

I don't get even; I get odder.

If at first you don't succeed, try again. But after the second failure, quit. No use being a damned fool about it.

Researchers say that during a lifetime, humans only use 12% of their brains. The other half will go to waste.

Geometry is the art of making correct conclusions based on incorrect pictures.

Numbers are like people—torture them long enough, and they'll tell you anything.

Approximately 50% of Americans have a below-average understanding of statistics.

The larger your sample size (N), the more confidence you can have that the sample mean is a fair representation of the population mean. In other words, the N justifies the means.

Here's a simple test: Take a fair coin, flip it repeatedly, and call out heads or tails before each flip. Very nearly half the time, you'll be asked to please stop.

If you study trigonometry, finding tangents will become secant nature!

A statistician is a person who draws a mathematically precise line from an unwarranted assumption to a foregone conclusion.

In Vatican City, there are two popes per square kilometer.

If a mathematician's dog is neutered, it can't multiply.

Some mathematicians are so negative, when they walk into a room, people look around and say, "Hey, who just left?"

In London, a pound of hamburger weighs about a pound.

The average statistician is just plain mean.

Light travels faster than sound. This is why some people appear bright until you hear them speak.

If 4 out of 5 people suffer from diarrhea... does that mean that 20% of people enjoy it?

My math teacher is like a Slinky... not really good for anything, but I can't help smiling when I see her tumble down the stairs.

If you multiply Santa Claus by i, does that make him real?

According to statistics, worrying works! Over 90% of the things we worry about never happen.

Factorials were someone's attempt to make math look exciting.

Algebra is x-sighting.

I'm partial to fractions.

I like angles... to a degree.

If a mathematician writes a fantasy novel, would the pages have imaginary numbers?

Statistics are like a bikini. What is revealed is interesting, but what is concealed is crucial.

I'm approximately 30% funny and 80% bad at math.

I was good at math, until they started mixing in the alphabet.

I could go on and on about infinite sequences.

Translations are shifty.

Complex numbers are unreal.

I feel positive about integers.

A topologist walks into a café and asks, "Can I have a doughnut of coffee, please?"

Mole problems? Just call 602-1023.

People who take a long time computing the ratio of rise to run are slope pokes.

The Hotel Infinity: Where there's always room for one more!

Whenever four mathematicians get together, you'll likely find a fifth.

After having our fill of sweet and sour pork, moo goo gai pan, and chow mein, we were still able to fill many boxes with leftovers to take home. But this was to be expected, as a result of the Chinese Remainder theorem.

A mathematician is standing at the photocopier and complaining to the secretary. "I set it to single-sided copy, and now it comes out as a Möbius strip!"

That suspicious man over there has some graph paper. I think he's plotting something.

The derivative of my enthusiasm for mathematics is positive for all values of the independent variable.

It Takes All Kinds

There are only 2 kinds of math books: those you cannot read beyond the first sentence, and those you cannot read beyond the first page.

(C. N. Yang, Nobel Prize in Physics, 1957)

There are 2 kinds of people in the world: those who don't do math, and those who take care of them.

There are 3 kinds of people in the world: positive, negative, and relative.

There are 2 kinds of people in the world: those who are wise, and those who are otherwise.

There are 2 kinds of statistics: the kind you look up, and the kind you make up.

There are 2 kinds of experienced actuaries: those who say they have made significant forecasting errors, and liars.

There are 10 kinds of people in the world: those who understand binary, and those who don't.

There are 10 kinds of people in the world: those who understand binary, and 9 others.

There are 10 kinds of people in the world: those who understand ternary; those who don't understand ternary; and, those who mistake it for binary.

There are 11 kinds of people in the world: those who can count in binary, and those who can't.

There are $8 - 3 \times 2$ kinds of people in the world: those who correctly apply the order of operations, and those who don't think that $6 \div 2 \times (1+2) = 9$.

There are $\int_3^5 \frac{x}{4}\, dx$ kinds of people in the world: those who understand Calculus, and those who don't.

There are 2 kinds of people in the world:
logicians $\wedge \sim$ logicians.

There are 2 kinds of people in the world: those who can't extrapolate from incomplete data.

Definitions

Actuary: where they bury dead actors.

Coeschatology: the study of the beginning of times; the coend is ming!

Computer: an actuary with a heart.

Conclusion: your last thought before you got tired of thinking.

Forum: twoum + twoum.

Hypotenuse: an occupied restroom on an airplane.

Joke: something that *almost* makes an engineer laugh.

Light Year: 365 days of drinking low-calorie beer.

Lite: the new way to spell "Light," now with 20% fewer letters.

Lottery: a tax on people who are bad at math.

Mathematics: physics without purpose.

Mixed Emotions: watching your math teacher drive over a cliff in your new Ferrari.

Multipliers: more than one pincer with parallel surfaces used for holding small objects.

Posterior Analysis: Checking out your significant other as he or she walks away.

Proof: one-half percent of alcohol.

Recursive: (λ damn. damn (damn)) (λ damn. damn (damn))

Residual Plots: The last few available graves in a cemetery.

Topologist: someone who doesn't know the difference between his ass and a hole in the ground, but who does know the difference between his ass and two holes in the ground.

Vector Space: a set V such that for any x in V, x has a little arrow over it.

Yard Sale: where you can buy a ruler that's 3 feet long.

Bumper Stickers and Fortune Cookies

You are a complex person, and *i* would like to be your friend.

When life throws you a curve, calculate the slope of the tangent at the point of inflection.

You will live a long life. If you marry a mathematician, it will feel even longer.

Your lucky number is $\sqrt{17}$.

Fame and fortune will find you… unless you lock yourself in an attic, trying to prove the Riemann Hypothesis.

Will you still need me, will you still feed me, when I'm 2^6?

You are good at solving problems. Textbooks fear you.

This cookie contains no fortune. (How unfortunate.)

Your students secretly agree that your head is not in proportion to your body.

A foolish man will try to write a better fortune than this, but a mathematician will find it sufficient to know that a better one exists.

When someone finds a counterexample to your proof, seek a different proof.

You are so smart that you do not need answer keys.

The fortune of this cookie is obvious.

You are good at geometry. Q.E.D.

Greet new friends with a handshake. At a math social, greet new friends with the handshake problem.

Do not follow the instructions in this fortune cookie.

Mathematicians never die. They just become irrational.

Calculus teachers never die. They just disintegrate.

Algebra teachers are x-perts.

There is a fine line between numerator and denominator.

Cheap eggs are a dime a dozen.

Don't talk… just invert and multiply. Fractions speak louder than words!

A penny for your thoughts... a dollar for your math homework!

Don't get too close... I'm an asymptote.

I turn coffee into theorems.

Think outside the regular quadrilateral.

Professional mathematician. Don't try this at home.

And Satan said, "Put the alphabet in math."

I brake for math jokes.

Don't discuss infinity. You'll never hear the end of it.

Math and science are for people who don't know how important football is.

I find your lack of math disturbing.

I do my own math stunts.

Honk if you know the thousandth digit of π!

Calculus is an integral part of life.

I've counted to infinity.

It only takes one person to make a statistically insignificant difference.

Topologists don't marry. They tie the knot.

Take a risk. Marry an actuary.

I'm not an outlier; I just haven't found my distribution yet.

Someday you will find a useful application for Ceva's theorem. (Maybe.)

I've found an elegant proof of Fermat's Last Theorem, but this fortune is too small to contain it.

Actuaries probably do it.

Actuaries do it without risk.

Actuaries do it until death, disability, or withdrawal.

Economists do it with varying rates of interest.

Mathematicians do it associatively.

Mathematicians do it commutatively.

Mathematicians do it constantly.

Number theorists do it discretely.

Mathematicians do it functionally.

Number theorists do it in fields.

Algebraists do it in groups.

Mathematicians do it in numbers.

Calculus teachers do it partially.

Calculus teachers do it continuously.

Calculus teachers do it by integrating their parts.

Mathematicians do it rationally.

Algebraists do it variably.

Statisticians probably do it.

Mathematicians do it with imaginary parts.

Mathematicians do it with their real parts.

Mathematicians do it with relations.

Calculus teachers do it without limits.

Mathematicians do it over an open, unmeasurable interval.

Mathematicians have to prove they did it.

(logicians do it) or ~(logicians do it).

Möbius always does it on the same side.

Mathematicians do it with Nobel's wife.

Mathematicians do it with a Minkowski sausage.

Algebraists do it with rings.

Algebraists do it in groups.

Old mathematicians never die; they just lose some of their functions.

Old calculus teachers never die; they just disintegrate.

Old statisticians never die; they just get broken down by age and sex.

Old actuaries never die; they just lose their reserve.

Tom Swifties

"I hate quizzes," Tom stated testily.

"1, 3, 5, 7, …," Tom said oddly.

"168 is a multiple of 2," Tom said evenly.

"6 is a special number," Tom said perfectly.

"Remove the braces," Tom remarked parenthetically.

"If p, then q," Tom implied.

"It is 12 inches long," Tom ruled.

"It's 5.1 meters," was Tom's measured response.

"They are mirror images," Tom reflected.

"Repeating decimals do not end," Tom remarked with infinite wisdom.

"This is a function," Tom related.

"1/2 is a fraction," said Tom properly.

"13/26 is a fraction," said Tom improperly.

"The decimal expansion of 1/3 is 0.3333333…," Tom repeated.

"It's not a segment; it's a ray," Tom said pointedly.

"3 = 11 mod 2," Tom noted basely.

"It touches the circle just once," Tom noted tangentially.

"Space is an infinite set of points," Tom said distantly.

"It must be a convex quadrilateral," Tom figured.

"1 = 1," Tom stated absolutely.

"18.96 is almost 19," Tom said roughly.

"It's a plane figure," Tom said flatly.

"Proofs are necessary," Tom reasoned.

"It's not the y-axis; it's not the y-axis; it's not the y-axis," Tom said inordinately.

"It's a vector," Tom directed.

"The square root of 2 cannot be written as a fraction!" Tom yelled irrationally.

"I don't know what $b^2 - 4ac$ equals, and I don't care!" Tom said indiscriminately.

"The concavity changes here," said Tom with inflection.

"e^x may be written as $1 + x/1! + x^2/2! + x^3/3! + \ldots$," Tom expanded.

"The function e^z is holomorphic," Tom analyzed.

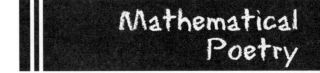

Mathematical Poetry

Writing haiku is
tough, because you have to count.
Writers stink at math.

Why are 15 and 16 bad poets?

Because they only relatively rhyme.

Everyone knows this old poem:

One for the money,
Two for the show,
Three to get ready,
And four to go!

But what are five and six?

Eleven!

To divide fractions:
Ours is not to reason why;
Just invert and multiply.

Smart

My dad gave me a one dollar bill
'Cause I'm his smartest son,
And I swapped it for two shiny quarters
'Cause two is more than one!

And then I took the quarters
And traded them to Lou
For three dimes—I guess he don't know
That three is more than two!

Just then, along came old blind Bates
And just 'cause he can't see
He gave me four nickels for my three dimes,
And four is more than three!

And I took the nickels to Hiram Coombs
Down at the seed-feed store,
And the fool gave me five pennies for them,
And five is more than four!

And then I went and showed my dad,
And he got red in the cheeks
And closed his eyes and shook his head—
Too proud of me to speak!

(Shel Silverstein)

Don't be dramatic;
It is just mathematics.
Easy: 1, 2, 3.

(winner of the 2012 Math Jokes 4 Mathy Folks online
poetry contest)

With my hands in a fire
And my feet on some ice
I'd say that, on average,
I feel rather nice.

One and one make two,
But if one and one should marry,
Isn't it queer
Within a year
There's two and one to carry?

Late in the fall semester,
Dressed in suede and polyester,
I was thinking 'bout a theorem I'd derived;
So drunk was I with mathy passion,
Into the gutter I went a-crashin',
And a pig came up and lay down at my side.

Yes, I lay there on my rear end
With my stinky, pinky new friend
When a woman passing by did softly say,
"You can tell a mathy creep
By the company he'll keep" —
And the pig got up and slowly walked away.

A dozen, a gross, and a score,
Plus three times the square root of four,
All divided by seven,
Plus five times eleven,
Equals nine squared, and not a bit more.

(Leigh Mercer, though often falsely attributed
to John Saxon)

'Tis a favorite project of mine
A new value of π to assign.
I would fix it at 3,
For that's simpler, you see,
Than 3.14159.

A mathematician named Joe
Said, "Really, it just can't be so;
"My wife, for her sins,
"Is going to have twins,
"And 2 into 1 doesn't go!"

Pick a number 1 to 9, I plea,
Then multiply by 15,873.
And again times seven,
The product to leaven;
A digit six times repeated you'll see.

A mathematician confided
That a Möbius strip is one-sided
And you'll get quite a laugh
When you cut one in half
For it stays in one piece when divided!

A topologist's child was quite hyper,
Till it wore a Möbius diaper.
The mess on the inside
Was thus on the outside,
And it was easy for someone to wipe her.

Points
Have no parts or joints
How then can they combine
To form a line?

(J. A. Lindon)

Pi goes on and on and on...
And *e* is likewise cursed.
I wonder: Which is larger
When their digits are reversed?

(J. A. Lindon)

Roses are #FF0000
Violets are #0000FF
Hexadecimal rocks,
And so do you!

Roses are #CC0000
Leaves are #00FF00
You rock as much
As the powers of 16!

If I let $k = 0$,
I can be a mathematical hero:
For if I decide
By k to divide,
Then it's clear that $1 = 0$.

A mathematician named Klein
Thought the Möbius band was divine.
Said he, "If you glue
The edges of two,
You get a weird bottle like mine."

To multiply two negatives:
Minus times minus is plus;
The reason for this we shall not discuss.

Square Root of Three

I fear that I will always be
A lonely number like root three.
A three is all that's good and right —
Why must my three keep out of sight
Beneath a vicious square root sign?
I wish, instead, I were a nine,
For nine could thwart this evil trick
With just some quick arithmetic.
I know I'll never see the sun
as one point seven three two one.
Such is my reality,
A sad irrationality.
When, hark, just what is this I see?
Another square root of three
Has quietly come waltzing by...
Together, now, we multiply,
And form a number we prefer
Rejoicing as an integer.
We break free from our mortal bonds
And with the wave of magic wands
Our square root signs become unglued
And love, for me, has been renewed.

(David Feinberg, recited in *Harold and Kumar Escape from Guantanamo Bay*)

A challenge for many long ages
Had baffled the savants and sages.
Yet at last came the light:
Seems old Fermat was right —
To the margin, add 200 pages.

I used to think math was no fun
'Cause I couldn't see how it was done.
But Euler's my hero
For I now see why 0
Equals $e^{i\pi} + 1$.

Fisher supposes kurtosis he knowses
But Bayes, he supposes more rigorously.

A conjecture both deep and profound
Is whether a circle is round.
In a paper of Erdös
Written in Kurdish
A counterexample is found.

In arctic and tropical climes,
the integers, addition, and times,
taken (mod p) will yield
a full finite field,
as p ranges over the primes.

Famous People

Gödel can't prove he was here.

Descartes thought he was here.

Heisenberg might have slept here.

I'm of two minds about this whole Schrödinger's cat thing...

What did Euclid order at McDonald's?
  A plane cheeseburger.

Was Newton easily susceptible to illness?
  Yes, that's why he called himself "I sick" Newton.

Mandelbrot often said he was born in Poland and educated in France, making him German, on average.

Jean-Paul Sartre is in a café. He says to the waitress, "I'd like a cup of coffee, please, with no cream."

The waitress replies, "I'm sorry, Monsieur, but we're out of cream. How about with no milk?"

Donald Knuth's wife says, "Honey, please run to the store and pick up a loaf of bread. If they have eggs, get a dozen." Knuth returns with 12 loaves of bread.

The great Russian scientist Ivan Ivanovich drops a thermometer and a candle from a third-floor window. He notices that they both reach the ground at the same time. Ivanovich concludes, "A thermometer falls at the speed of light."

Did you hear about the one-line proof of Fermat's Last Theorem?

It's identical to Andrew Wiles's proof, but it's written on a really long strip of paper.

Heisenberg gets stopped on the motorway by the police. The cop asks him, "Do you know how fast you were going?"

Heisenberg responds, "No, but I know exactly where I am."

Why was Heisenberg's wife unsatisfied?

When he had the time, he didn't have the energy; and when he had the position, he didn't have the momentum.

Alan Turing calls John Nash on the phone. "How's it going?" he asks.

"Great!" Nash replies.

"Sorry," says Turing. "I must have the wrong number."

Werner Heisenberg, Kurt Gödel and Noam Chomsky walk into a bar. Heisenberg looks around the bar and says, "Because there are three of us, and because this is a bar, it must be a joke. But the question remains, is it funny or not?"

Gödel thinks for a moment. "Well, because we're inside the joke, we can't tell whether it's funny or not. We'd have to be outside looking at it."

Chomsky looks at both of them. "Of course it's funny," he says. "You're just telling it wrong."

Pythagoras is hip to b^2.

What do you get when you cross Einstein and Pythagoras?

$$E = m \times (a^2 + b^2)$$

Einstein, Newton and Pascal are playing hide-and-seek. Einstein covers his eyes and starts counting to 10. Pascal runs and hides, but Newton draws a one-meter by one-meter square on the ground in front of Einstein and then stands in the middle of it. When Einstein opens his eyes and sees Newton, he yells, "Newton! I found you! You're it!"

Newton smiles and replies, "You didn't find me. You found Pascal. I'm one Newton per square meter!"

Why do truncated McLaurin Series fit original functions so well?

Because they're Taylor-made.

When Cochise was very sick, the chiefs from other tribes came to pay their respects. Many of the braves in Cochise's tribe were surprised to see so many visitors. One brave, however, said that he was not surprised. He told the others, "I expect other chiefs to converge there because of Cochise condition."

Why are topologists susceptible to sleeping sickness?

It comes from the Tietze fly!

How do we know that Riemann was short?

He was often seen with stilts (Stieltjes).

$$\boxed{O}\boxed{P}\boxed{I}\boxed{N}\boxed{I}\boxed{O}\boxed{N} - \pi =$$

Cow-culator

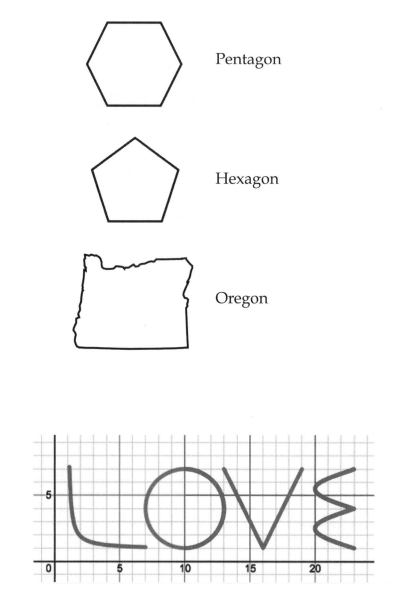

Pentagon

Hexagon

Oregon

$$\frac{\sin k}{\cos k} =$$

Hendecagon

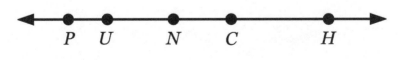

Punch Line

$$\left(\sqrt{-shit}\right)^2$$

Shit Just Got Real

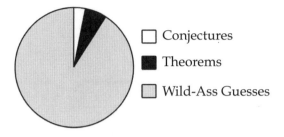

Mathematician's Work

Axis

Pythagorean Serum

Pure Math

Equations:

- crazy = talking to yourself – (cell phone + ear piece)
- maturity = things you used to do – things you used to do
- compassion = (what if that were me?) + (I'm glad that's not me)

An octopus declared, "I invented a number system based on 10. I'm just not sure it has any practical applications."

$\pi = 3$, for sufficiently large 3 and sufficiently small π.

The sum of two even primes is always a square.

An infinite number of mathematicians walk into a bakery. The first orders a pie, the second orders a quarter of a pie, the third a ninth of a pie, and so on. The baker says, "I see what's going on here." He bakes one pie, cuts off the round edges, and divides it into six pieces.

Why do they call it center city?

Because everyone commutes there.

You know you're a mathematician if you've ever wondered how Euler pronounced Euclid.

Consider the set of all sets that have never been considered. Hey, they're all gone!

I went to visit her while she was lying ill at the hospital. I had come in taxi cab number 14 and remarked that it was a rather dull number. "No," she replied, "it is a very interesting number. It's the smallest number expressible as the product of 7 and 2 in two different ways."

The Yoda embedding, contravariant it is.

What's big, grey, and proves the uncountability of the reals?

Cantor's diagonal elephant.

Delta is sitting at home bored, watching TV. The doorbell rings, and Delta gets up to answer. Upon opening the door, she finds Epsilon standing there. "Epsilon! What are you doing here?"

Epsilon answers, "Oh, I was just in the neighborhood."

Why is it difficult to have a snowball fight in Hilbert space?

Because the snow doesn't compact very well.

An infinite number of mathematicians walk into a bank. The first asks to withdraw one dollar, the second for half a dollar, the third for one third of a dollar, and so on. The banker thinks for a minute, then tells them to leave.

Bars and Restaurants

What's the difference between a mathematician and a coconut?

>You can get a drink out of a coconut.

A guy in a bar says to the guy next to him, "Hey, you want to hear a joke about some stupid engineers?"

The other guy replies, "Well, before you tell that joke, you should know that I'm 6'2", 200 pounds, and I'm an engineer. And my buddy here is 6'4", 250 pounds, and he's an engineer, too. Now, do you still want to tell your joke?"

The first guy says, "Maybe you're right. I don't have the energy to explain it twice."

What does a vegan mathematician eat?

>Roots, whole numbers, natural logs, tree diagrams, and stem-and-leaf plots.

Did you hear about the restaurant that opened on the moon?

>Good food, but absolutely *no* atmosphere.

Recently overheard at the Icosagon Cafe:

- "Sure, he's degenerate, but I say, 'Let bigons be bigons!'"
- "I don't have the energy for another attempt. Trigon."
- "I took an antidote for the wizard's curse. Hexagon."
- "I just looked at the calendar. Septagon. Octagon. Nov is here!"
- "Nonagon. They're all here!"
- "Someone stole my pack of cards. Decagon."
- "My parrot just died. Polygon."

To place an order, press 1.

For a staff directory, press 2.

To file a complaint, press $\sqrt{67}$.

A hungry man went into a restaurant and was amazed to find that rabbit burgers were only 49¢ each. When he asked the cook why they were so cheap, the cook said that some filler had been added to keep the price low.

"What kind of filler?" the man asked.

"Horse meat," the cook replied.

The man asked, "How much of each kind of meat is in a burger?"

"Equal amounts," the cook said. "One horse, one rabbit."

Pavlov is enjoying a pint at the pub when a phone rings. He jumps up and shouts, "Damn! I forgot to feed the dog!"

A man walks into a bar and orders six shots of tequila. He lines them up and downs the first, third and fifth glasses.

"Excuse me," says the bartender, "but you didn't touch three of the glasses."

The man replies, "Well, my doctor said it's okay for me to have the odd drink."

What do you say to a guy who walks into a bar three times?
    "Move the bar, stupid!"

A statistician, an accountant, and a notary walk into a bar. They order beers. When the beers arrive, the statistician smells his and says, "If I drink this, I'll probably die."

The accountant looks at the tab and says, "Don't drink it; you can't afford it, anyway."

The notary says, "You said it!"

A number theorist goes into a bar... exactly eleven times.

A female mathematician walks into a bar. A guy comes up to her and says, "Hey baby, what's your sign?"

She says, "One over my cosecant."

A neutron goes into a bar and orders a beer. As the neutron is reaching for its wallet, the bartender looks at it and says, "Oh, don't bother. For you—no charge."

Two cannibals are eating dinner. The son says, "I really hate my math professor." His mother replies, "Fine, then just eat the noodles."

Two cannibals are eating a number theorist. One says to the other, "Does this taste odd to you?"

Two cannibals are eating their college math professor. One says to the other, "I told you we'd eventually get even with him."

Two cannibals are eating a math teacher. One says to the other, "Does this taste chalky to you?"

Two cannibals are eating a statistician. One says to the other, "Does this taste normal to you?"

Two cannibals are eating an actuary. One says to the other, "This is a little bland."

Schrodinger's cat walks into a bar. And doesn't.

An infinite number of mathematicians walk into a bar. The first one orders a beer, the second one orders half a beer, the third one orders a quarter of a beer, and so on. After a while of this happening, the bartender says, "Come on folks! So many people and not even a couple of beers?"

An infinite number of mathematicians walk into the Fibonacci bar.

The first says, "I'll have a beer, please."

The second says, "I'll have a beer, also."

The nth mathematician points to the two guys that just ordered and says, "I'll have what she's having, and then I'll have what he's having."

Every Friday night, a mathematician goes to the pub, sits on the next-to-last stool, turns to the last stool, and asks a non-existent woman if she would like a drink. The mathematician returns every Friday night during the school year, yet the bartender says nothing.

Finally, the last Friday before summer break, the bartender asks the mathematician, "Excuse me, sir. You are clearly aware that there is no woman sitting in that chair. Why do you keep talking to an empty stool?"

The mathematician responds, "According to quantum mechanics, an empty space is not really void. Virtual particles materialize and disappear at every instant. Nobody knows whether an appropriate wave function will collapse in such a way that a beautiful girl will appear out of nowhere."

The bartender raises his eyebrow. "Really? That's interesting. But couldn't you just ask one of the women already in the bar if she'd like a drink? Who knows, maybe one of them would say yes."

The mathematician laughs. "Oh, sure!" he says. "And what's the probability of *that* happening?"

An actuary is talking to a person at a bar. The person asks, "What do you do for a living?"

The actuary responds, "I model."

The person, now intrigued, responds, "Really? What kind of modeling?"

The actuary answers, "Financial, bootstrap, predictive, proxy, whatever it takes!"

And the bartender says, "We don't serve tachyons here." A tachyon walks into a bar.

A good bartender knows to cut off calculus teachers before they reach their limit.

Two mathematicians walk into a restaurant for lunch. One challenges the other to a wager, and the loser will pay the bill. The challenger says, "I guarantee that the waiter won't know the correct expansion of $(a + b)^2$."

"You're on!" replied her colleague.

They place their order, and the waiter is asked for the expansion of $(a + b)^2$. The waiter replies, "Obviously, it's $a^2 + b^2$."

"Ha!" says the challenger. "I told you he wouldn't know!"

To which the waiter adds, "Provided, of course, that a and b are anticommutative."

Knock, Knock

Knock, knock.
Who's there?
Lemma.
Lemma who?
Lemma in, it's raining!

Knock, knock.
Who's there?
Mode.
Mode who?
Mode the lawn. What should I do next?

Knock, knock.
Who's there?
Slope.
Slope who?
Slope ups should stay on the porch.

Knock, knock.
Who's there?
Convex.
Convex who?
Convex go to prison!

Knock, knock.
Who's there?
Prism.
Prism who?
Prism is where convex go!
(Weren't you paying attention to the previous joke?)

Knock, knock.
Who's there?
Origin.
Origin who?
Vodka martini origin fizz?

Knock, knock.
Who's there?
Unit.
Unit who?
Unit socks; I knit sweaters.

Knock, knock.
Who's there?
Outlier.
Outlier who?
Outlier! We only let honest people in this house!

Knock, knock.
Who's there?
Möbius.
Möbius who?
Möbius a big whale!

Knock, knock.
Who's there?
Tangents.
Tangents who?
Tangents spend a lot of time at the beach.

Knock, knock.
Who's there?
Axis.
Axis who?
Axis for chopping, saw is for cutting.

Knock, knock.
Who's there?
Zeroes.
Zeroes who?
Zeroes as fast as she can, but the boat doesn't move.

ORDER FORM
CALL (541) 347-9882 or FAX (541) 347-9883
Or COPY and mail in to Robert D. Reed Publishers
P.O. Box 1992, Bandon, OR 97411
Or shop and order online at www.rdrpublishers.com

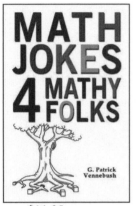

$11.95 _____

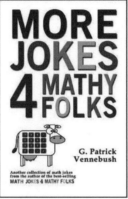

$11.95 _____

$9.95 _____

$9.95 _____

$9.95 _____

$11.95 _____

Quantity of books ordered _____ Total amount for books _____

Shipping ($3.95 for orders under $25 and FREE for orders over $25.00) _____

FINAL TOTAL _____